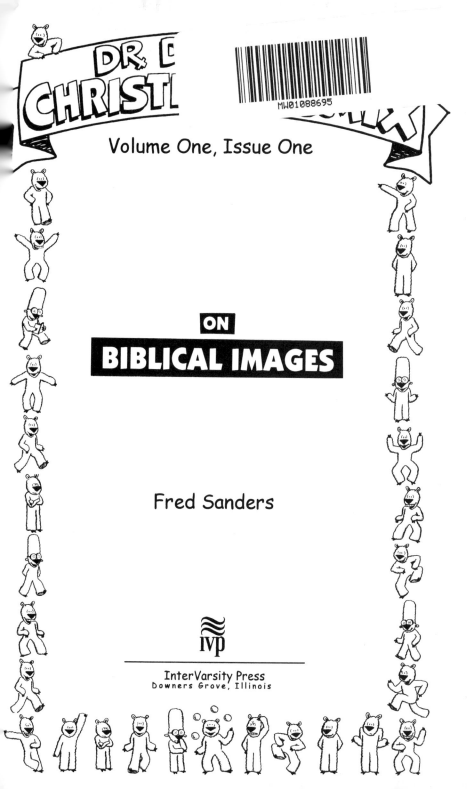

DR. D
CHRIST

Volume One, Issue One

ON
BIBLICAL IMAGES

Fred Sanders

IVP

InterVarsity Press
Downers Grove, Illinois

InterVarsity Press® is the book-publishing division of InterVarsity Christian
Fellowship/USA®, a student movement active on campus at hundreds of
universities, colleges and schools of nursing in the United States of America, and a
member movement of the International Fellowship of Evangelical Students. For
information about local and regional activities, write Public Relations Dept.,
InterVarsity Christian Fellowship/USA, 6400 Schroeder Rd., P.O. Box 7895,
Madison, WI 53707-7895.

In most cases Scripture quotations are taken from the *New Revised Standard
Version* of the Bible, copyright 1989 by the Division of Christian Education of the
National Council of the Churches of Christ in the USA. Used by permission. All
rights reserved.

ISBN 0-8308-2241-0

Printed in the United States of America ♻

15 14 13 12 11 10 9 8 7 6 5 4 3 2 1
10 09 08 07 06 05 04 03 02 01 00 99

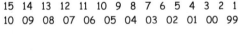

InterVarsity Press
P.O. Box 1400
Downers Grove, IL 60515

World Wide Web: www.ivpress.com

E-mail: mail@ivpress.com

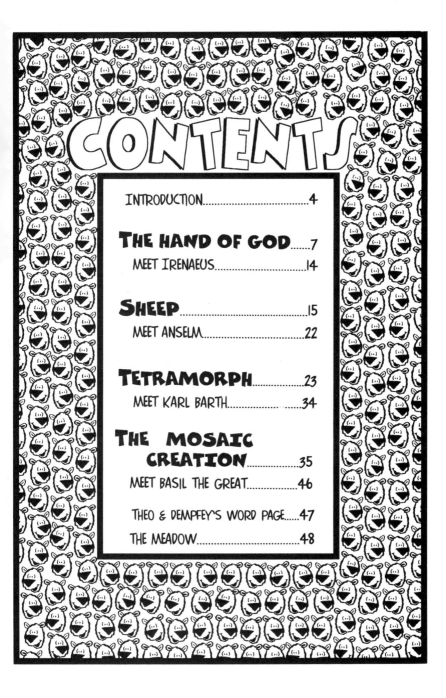

CONTENTS

INTRODUCTION

ANOTHER BUSY DAY AT DR. DOCTRINE'S THEOLOGY CLINIC...

HELLO, *THEO!* WHAT CAN I HELP YOU WITH TODAY?

WELL, DOCTOR, I'M NOT SURE *HOW* TO CHARACTERIZE MY *MALADY*. I SEEM TO BE SUFFERING FROM A CASE OF GENERAL *DISORIENTATION* OR *CONFUSION*.

RECENTLY I'VE BEEN HAVING TROUBLE GETTING MY *BEARINGS* AND *FINDING* MY *WAY* FROM PLACE TO PLACE.

IT'S VERY *DISORIENTING*, I ASSURE YOU.

UM. *THEO.* I'M OVER *HERE.*

EH?

OH!

THERE! SEE, IT HAPPENED *AGAIN!* FOR *NO* APPARENT REASON PEOPLE AND OBJECTS SEEM TO BE *MOVING AROUND* UNPREDICTABLY. FOR EXAMPLE TREES AND ROCKS HAVE BEEN *LEAPING* IN FRONT OF ME WITHOUT WARNING.

EVEN MY *BIBLE STUDY* IS SUFFERING. THE WORDS SEEM MEANINGLESS AND UNCONNECTED.

ASK DR. DOCTRINE

SAY "AAAAHH BELIEVE!"

DEAR DR. DOCTRINE,

WHAT'S THIS "THEOLOGY" STUFF, ANYWAY?

GOOD QUESTION!

YOU PROBABLY RECOGNIZE THE LAST PART OF THE WORD; THE SUFFIX "-OLOGY." IT USUALLY MEANS "THE STUDY OF" OR "THE SCIENCE OF" SOMETHING.

AS IN, BIOLOGY...

-OLOGY

OR GEOLOGY...

PHRENOLOGY...

PALEONTOLOGY...

WELL, "THEOS" IS THE GREEK WORD FOR "GOD," SO WHEN YOU ADD IT TO THE FRONT OF "-OLOGY," YOU GET "THE SCIENCE OF GOD," WHICH IS A PRETTY GOOD DESCRIPTION OF THEOLOGY!

THEOLOGY

EVEN THOUGH IT SOUNDS SORT OF COCKY...

THIS RAISES THE QUESTION, HOW DO YOU STUDY GOD? I MEAN, OTHER SCIENCES HAVE SPECIAL INSTRUMENTS, BUT AS FAR AS I KNOW, THERE'S NO SUCH THING AS A GOD-O-SCOPE, OR A THEOGRAPH, OR A GOD-OMETER...

OR EVEN SAFETY GOD-GLES...

WHICH IS WHY THEOLOGY HAS TO TAKE ITS STARTING POINT FROM GOD'S OWN SELF-REVELATION! THE SCIENCE OF GOD HAS TO START WHERE GOD TELLS IT TO!

FURTHERMORE, IF THERE IS SOME SORT OF INSTRUMENT FOR RECEIVING THIS REVELATION, IT MUST BE YOUR WHOLE HEART...IN FACT YOUR WHOLE SELF, WITH AS FEW SMUDGES ON YOUR LENSES AND DIALS AS POSSIBLE...

IF YOU WANT TO UNDER-STAND GOD, YOU REALLY HAVE TO OBEY GOD!

TO BE MORE PRECISE, GOD'S REVELATION CAN REALLY ONLY BE DEALT WITH IN A COMMUNITY OF SUCH INSTRUMENTS, SO THEY CAN CHECK UP ON EACH OTHER AND BECOME MORE SENSITIVE.

SO THAT'S THEOLOGY: THE SCIENTIFIC STUDY OF GOD'S SELF-REVELATION CARRIED OUT IN THE CONTEXT OF A SANCTIFIED CHURCH!

OF COURSE, I COULD SAY MORE....

THAT'S MY ANSWER!

9

IF YOU SPEND SOME TIME LOOKING THROUGH THE BIBLE FOR SIMILAR REFERENCES, YOU'LL COME UP WITH GOD HAVING *EYES, EARS, FEET, GUTS, FEATHERS, WINGS...*

SO ONE WAY OF LOOKING AT IT IS THAT EVEN THOUGH THE BIBLE *SEEMS* TO SAY THAT GOD HAS HANDS, IT'S JUST A FIGURE OF SPEECH, A WAY OF SAYING THAT GOD HAS *POWER!*

IN OTHER WORDS, GOD DOESN'T *REALLY* HAVE HANDS!

BUT ON THE OTHER...UH...*HAND*... IF "HAND" IS ANOTHER WAY OF SAYING "POWER" THEN CERTAINLY GOD ABOVE ALL OTHERS HAS A HAND.

IN FACT, NOBODY ELSE'S ARE REALLY WORTHY OF BEING PUT IN THE SAME CATEGORY WITH GOD'S... GOD'S HAND IS THE HAND TO END ALL HANDS!

IN OTHER WORDS, *ONLY* GOD HAS HANDS!

I KNOW THAT SEEMS SORT OF *BACKWARDS,* BUT IT'S THE ONLY WAY TO TALK ABOUT GOD WITHOUT SMUGGLING IN ALL SORTS OF PRECONCEIVED IDEAS.

IF YOU START BY SAYING "I HAVE HANDS AND SO DOES GOD," YOU'RE REALLY TAKING HUMAN ATTRIBUTES AND *PROJECTING* THEM ONTO GOD! AND IF YOU TAKE THEM LITERALLY, THEN YOU END UP WITH A GOD WHO IS REALLY JUST *YOURSELF* PROJECTED ONTO THE HEAVENS!

WHAT'S THAT CALLED WHEN YOU ATTRIBUTE HUMAN CHARACTERISTICS TO SOMETHING THAT'S NOT HUMAN?

ANTHROPOMORPHISM!

YEAH, OR A TALKING SHEEP!

LIKE A GOD WITH HANDS?

OR TALKING MOTHS?

ONCE YOU START PROJECTING, *EVERYBODY* WANTS TO GET INTO THE ACT....

GOD IS BIG AND STRONG. OBVIOUSLY HE IS AN *OX!*

NAY! GOD IS IN FACT A MIGHTY *HORSE!*

I KNOW YOU MEANT TO SAY "*LION*," SO I'LL LET IT SLIDE THIS TIME. GRRRRRRR....

IT IS TRUE, THE *GREAT DUCK* IS LIKE ALL OF THESE THINGS, IN CERTAIN WAYS...

BELIEVE ME, THIS IS ONE GAME YOU DON'T EVEN WANT TO *START* PLAYING! NOBODY WINS, AND THERE'S NO WAY TO *STOP* IT!

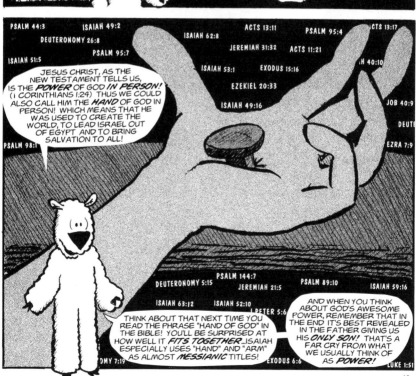

MEET THE THEOLOGIANS

IRENAEUS
OF LYONS
BORN AROUND 150

IRENAEUS WAS THE BISHOP OF LYONS, FRANCE, IN THE SECOND CENTURY. HE WAS THE FIRST THINKER TO EXPLAIN THE WHOLE SCOPE OF CHRISTIAN DOCTRINE IN A COMPREHENSIVE WAY. ALTHOUGH HE NEVER SAT DOWN AND WROTE OUT A REAL "SYSTEMATIC THEOLOGY" (PARTLY BECAUSE HE WAS TOO BUSY TAKING CARE OF THE IMMEDIATE NEEDS OF THE CHURCHES UNDER HIS CARE), STILL HE CLEARLY DESERVES THE TITLE THAT HE IS SOMETIMES GIVEN, "THE FOUNDER OF CHRISTIAN THEOLOGY."

IRENAEUS IS AN ESPECIALLY VALUABLE WITNESS TO THE ROOTS OF CHRISTIANITY BECAUSE HE LIVED AND WORKED WITHIN A FEW GENERATIONS OF THE APOSTLES. AS A BOY, HE KNEW THE FAMOUS MARTYR, POLYCARP, WHO WAS A DISCIPLE OF THE APOSTLE JOHN HIMSELF! WHEN CERTAIN HERETICS CAUSED TROUBLE BY CLAIMING TO HAVE "INSIDE INFORMATION" THAT THEY GOT FROM A "SECRET TRADITION," IRENAEUS WAS ABLE TO REFUTE THEM WITH AUTHORITY!

GO MAKE DISCIPLES!

TAG! YOU'RE IT!

IT ONLY TAKES A SPARK...

ALTHOUGH HIS NAME MEANS "PEACE," IRENAEUS HAD TO SPEND A LOT OF HIS TIME AND ENERGY FIGHTING. MOST OF ALL HE FOUGHT THESE "SECRET TRADITION" HERETICS, KNOWN AS "GNOSTICS." AMONG OTHER BIZARRE THINGS THEY TAUGHT, THEY BELIEVED IN A WHOLE HOST OF GODS, SUB-GODS, AND DEMI-GODS WHO COUPLED WITH EACH OTHER TO POPULATE THE HEAVENS. AGAINST SUCH SPECULATIONS IRENAEUS INSISTED THAT THERE IS ONLY ONE TRUE GOD!

BECAUSE HE HAD TO BE VIGILANT IN DEFENDING THE UNITY OF GOD, IRENAEUS HAD TO BE VERY CAREFUL ABOUT HOW HE DESCRIBED THE TRINITY! OF COURSE BACK THEN, THE WORD "TRINITY" HADN'T EVEN BEEN MADE UP YET. WHEN IRENAEUS TALKED ABOUT THE SON AND THE SPIRIT, HE DESCRIBED THEM AS "THE TWO HANDS OF GOD," WHICH GOD USES TO CARRY OUT HIS WILL IN THE WORLD. HE DIDN'T MEAN THAT THEY WERE JUST DIVINE APPENDAGES, BUT THAT WE SHOULD THINK OF GOD'S WORD AND SPIRIT AS NOTHING LESS THAN GOD HIMSELF IN ACTION!

SINCE THE NEW TESTAMENT WAS MOSTLY ASSEMBLED BY THIS TIME, IRENAEUS WAS A PART OF THE FIRST GENERATION OF CHRISTIANS TO HAVE ALMOST THE WHOLE BIBLE TO WORK WITH (HE STILL LACKED HEBREWS AND A FEW EPISTLES). HE WAS ABLE TO READ THE WHOLE THING AND TRY TO GET A GRIP ON THE ENTIRE STORY IT TOLD. THE WAY IRENAEUS UNDERSTOOD IT, THE MAIN THEME OF THE BIBLE IS HOW GOD HAS ESTABLISHED A RELATIONSHIP WITH HUMANITY THROUGH A SERIES OF COVENANTS FROM ADAM TO CHRIST...

ADAM NOAH ABRAHAM MOSES DAVID CHRIST

ALL OF GOD'S WAYS WITH US BEGIN AND END IN CHRIST, WHO BECAME INCARNATE AMONG US IN ORDER TO FULFILL ALL THE PROMISES OF THE COVENANTS. JESUS LIVED THROUGH THE WHOLE HUMAN EXPERIENCE AND MADE IT HIS OWN. IRENAEUS CALLED THIS "RECAPITULATING" HUMANITY, OR GATHERING UP THE WHOLE WORK AND BRINGING IT TO FULFILLMENT. THUS CHRIST IS "THE SECOND ADAM" WHO RESTORES WHAT THE FIRST ONE LOST!

HE BECAME LIKE US SO THAT WE COULD BECOME LIKE HIM!

SHEEP

NARRATED BY THAT AMAZING GRAZER

MEET THE THEOLOGIANS ANSELM

ASK DR. DOCTRINE

TAKE TWO TESTAMENTS AND CALL ME IN THE MORNING!

DEAR DOC,

WHAT'S SO *"SYSTEMATIC"* ABOUT THIS *THEOLOGY STUFF,* ANYWAY?

GOOD QUESTION!

SYSTEMATIC THEOLOGY IS JUST THEOLOGY THAT TRIES TO TAKE IN THE *WHOLE* RANGE OF CHRISTIAN DOCTRINE AS *ONE UNIFIED WHOLE...*

IF THAT'S NOT TOO OVERLY REDUNDANT...

CHRISTIANS BELIEVE AN AWFUL LOT OF STUFF, AND IF YOU'RE NOT CAREFUL, YOU END UP FEELING LIKE IT'S JUST A BIG *SHOPPING LIST* OF UNRELATED ITEMS!

GOD
JESUS
CHURCH
BIRDS
DIRT
BAPTISM
CREATION
DON'T CUSS
BIBLE
EASTER
HOLY STUFF
STEEPLES
FORGIVENESS
GOD
TREES
ANGELS
JESUS
UHH.....ETC.

...OR A PILE OF *ROCKS* THAT YOU'VE NEVER REALLY SORTED THROUGH. SYSTEMATIC THEOLOGY *SORTS* THROUGH THE ROCKS TO MAKE SURE THEY ALL BELONG IN THE SAME *PILE.*

I'M PRETTY SURE THIS *FROG* DOESN'T BELONG HERE.

WWWW.ANNABET?

THEN THE THEOLOGIAN PUTS THEM ALL TOGETHER IN A *SYSTEM,* A COHERENT ARRANGEMENT OF SOME KIND, PUTTING *EACH* ROCK WHERE IT BELONGS IN RELATION TO THE *OTHERS!*

HEY, BRAINIAC! YOU LEFT OUT THE SECOND COMING!

WHOOPS! BETTER START OVER!

ALL OF US HAVE *SOME* KIND OF SYSTEM IN OUR MINDS, SOME WAY OF *RELATING* ALL OUR BELIEFS TO EACH OTHER AND *DECIDING* WHICH ONES ARE MOST IMPORTANT! IT'S ONLY NATURAL!

NOT ME, BUDDY! I JUST BELIEVE WHAT MY *SCOFIELD* BIBLE TELLS ME!

THE ONLY THING THAT MAKES SYSTEMATIC THEOLOGIANS SPECIAL IS THAT THEY TRY TO TELL YOU RIGHT UP FRONT *WHY* THEY'VE ARRANGED THINGS THE WAY THEY HAVE...

AND TO SHOW AS CLEARLY AS POSSIBLE HOW IT ALL *FITS* TOGETHER!

SO THERE YOU HAVE IT: THE MAIN CONCERN OF SYSTEMATIC THEOLOGY IS TO EXPLAIN HOW ALL THE DOCTRINES FIT WITH EACH OTHER IN ONE SYSTEMATIC WHOLE!

THAT'S MY ANSWER!

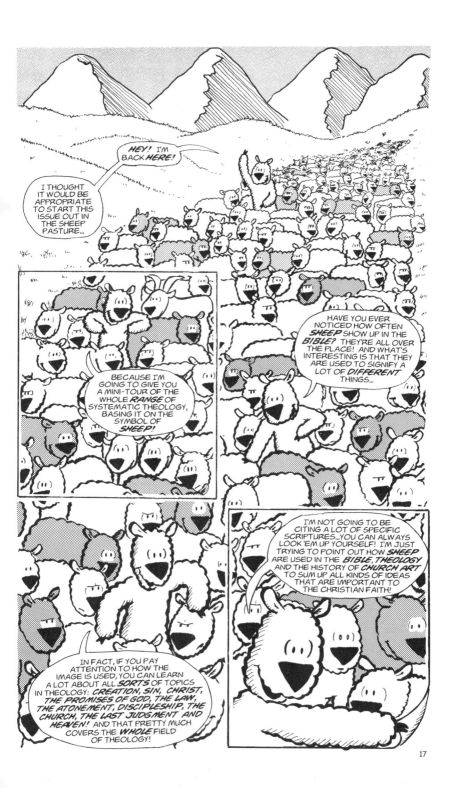

FIRST OF ALL, IT ALMOST GOES WITHOUT SAYING THAT SHEEP ARE GOD'S **CREATURES!** GOD MADE THEM—THAT IS, GOD MADE **US**—AND THAT'S PLENTY OF REASON TO PRAISE HIM! **PSALM 95:7** MAKES THIS CLEAR, WHERE IT SAYS....

--BY THE WAY, THIS IS THE **LAST** SCRIPTURE I'M GIVING YOU. WE'RE DOING **SYMBOLS** TODAY, NOT **TEXTS!** MY MOMMA DIDN'T RAISE ME TO BE YOUR CONCORDANCE!

ANYWAY, PSALM 95:6 & 7. "COME LET US WORSHIP AND BOW DOWN. LET US KNEEL BEFORE THE LORD OUR MAKER; FOR HE IS OUR GOD, AND WE ARE THE **PEOPLE** OF HIS **PASTURE**, AND THE **SHEEP** OF HIS **HAND**."

NOTICE HOW **NATURAL** IT IS FOR THE PSALMIST TO CALL US **PEOPLE** AND **SHEEP** AT THE SAME TIME?

CREATURES ARE CREATURES, AFTER ALL! OBVIOUSLY, THERE ARE PLENTY OF DIFFERENCES BETWEEN PEOPLE AND SHEEP, BUT GOD MADE US ALL, AND IT'S GOOD TO RECALL SOMETIMES WHAT IT MEANS TO BE A PART OF GOD'S ONE CREATION...

HEY... WHERE'D EVERYBODY GO?

WELL, THAT BRINGS ME TO MY NEXT POINT: SHEEP ARE CONSTANTLY REFERRED TO IN THE BIBLE AS BEING PRONE TO **WANDER OFF** IN THEIR OWN DIRECTIONS. AND THAT'S NOT A BAD IMAGE FOR HUMAN SIN: ALL **WE** LIKE SHEEP HAVE GONE ASTRAY...

GETTING LOST IN THE DARK...

DRINKING ROTTEN WATER...

GETTING STRANDED IN THE DARNDEST PLACES...

...NOW HOW DID I GET OUT HERE?

AND FALLING OFF THE OCCASIONAL CLIFF.

OF COURSE, THAT LAMB IS *ALSO* THE *GOOD SHEPHERD*, WHO GOES OUT IN SEARCH OF THE *LOST SHEEP*, WHO HAVE WANDERED AWAY!

IT'S BELIEVED THAT NON-CHRISTIAN *ROMANS* ALREADY HAD "GOOD SHEPHERD" STATUES THAT THEY USED AS SYMBOLS OF GENTLENESS AND GENEROSITY...

RIGHT AWAY, CHRISTIANS TOOK OVER THE IMAGE AS THEIR *OWN*, SINCE THEY KNEW THAT THE *REAL* GOOD SHEPHERD IS THE ONE WHO LAYS DOWN HIS *LIFE* FOR THE SHEEP!

OF COURSE, THE GOOD SHEPHERD DOES A LOT MORE THAN JUST GO OUT AFTER SHEEP WHO GET LOST! HE ALSO TAKES CARE OF THE NEEDS OF THE WHOLE FLOCK THAT IS UNDER HIS CONSTANT CARE...

HE LEADS THEM TO STILL WATERS AND GREEN PASTURES, HE ANOINTS THEM WITH OIL, HE PACKS A MEAN ROD AND STAFF TO WARD OFF PREDATORS...DOES ANY OF THIS SOUND *FAMILIAR?*

AND AS FUN AS THE JOURNEY MAY BE, THERE IS A DEFINITE *GOAL*: AT THE END OF THE TRIP, THE FLOCK COMES TO REST IN THE KINGDOM!

20

MEET THE THEOLOGIANS

ANSELM
OF CANTERBURY
1033-1109

ANSELM, ARCHBISHOP OF CANTERBURY, WAS AMONG THE FIRST OF THAT GROUP OF GREAT MEDIEVAL THINKERS KNOWN AS THE SCHOLASTICS. HIS ORIGINALITY AS A THEOLOGIAN ALMOST BOGGLES THE MIND! PERHAPS MORE THAN ANY OTHER THEOLOGIAN, ANSELM WAS PASSIONATE ABOUT THINKING... HIS PRAYER LIFE AND HIS THEOLOGICAL MEDITATIONS ARE NOT SEPARATE FROM EACH OTHER; IN FACT, HE WROTE SOME OF HIS MOST PROFOUND BOOKS IN THE FORM OF EXTENDED PRAYERS.

AS A LITTLE BOY, ANSELM BELIEVED THAT GOD LIVED ON TOP OF THE BIG MOUNTAINS HE COULD SEE FROM HIS HOUSE. HE ONCE HAD A VISION THAT HE CLIMBED THE MOUNTAIN AND CAME INTO THE COURTS OF HEAVEN, WHERE GOD POLITELY ASKED HIM HIS NAME. THEY HAD A NICE TALK, THEN AN ANGEL GAVE ANSELM SOME BREAD AND SENT HIM BACK HOME.

ANSELM REMEMBERED EVERY DETAIL OF THIS VISION EVEN WHEN HE WAS AN OLD MAN. IT MAY NOT BE GOING TOO FAR TO SAY THAT ANSELM ALWAYS LOOKED AT THE SPIRITUAL AND INTELLECTUAL LIFE AS A KIND OF MOUNTAIN-CLIMBING ADVENTURE.

ANSELM IS MOST FAMOUS FOR A PROOF OF THE EXISTENCE OF GOD. THE ONTOLOGICAL ARGUMENT, AS IT IS CALLED, STARTS WITH THE IDEA OF GOD, AN IDEA OF SOMETHING "SO GREAT THAT NOTHING GREATER CAN BE THOUGHT OF." THEN ANSELM ARGUES THAT IT'S GREATER TO EXIST IN REALITY THAN IN THOUGHT ONLY, SO THIS GREATEST IDEA MUST EXIST IN REALITY. PEOPLE EITHER GET THIS ARGUMENT OR THEY DON'T...IT STILL HAS FANS TODAY.

ANOTHER IDEA THAT ANSELM HAD THAT IS STILL WITH US TODAY IS THE SATISFACTION THEORY OF THE ATONEMENT. BEFORE ANSELM, MOST THEOLOGIANS TALKED ABOUT THE CROSS AS A KIND OF RANSOM WHICH WAS PAID TO THE DEVIL, WHO HAD GAINED LEGAL RIGHTS TO OUR SOULS THROUGH SIN. SOMETIMES THEY EVEN TALKED ABOUT JESUS TRICKING SATAN INTO LETTING HIS PRISONERS GO FREE, BY BAITING THE HOOK OF THE CROSS WITH HIS HUMANITY, THEN CONQUERING DEATH AS GOD.

ANSELM CHANGED THE EMPHASIS ALTOGETHER: INSTEAD OF LOOKING AT SIN AS SOMETHING THAT TRANSFERS OUR OWNERSHIP OVER TO THE DEVIL, HE LOOKED AT IT AS AN OFFENSE AGAINST GOD'S HONOR! SINCE GOD IS INFINITELY HOLY, ONLY AN INFINITE REPAYMENT CAN SATISFY HIS WOUNDED HONOR. TODAY THIS WAY OF TALKING MIGHT SOUND A LITTLE BIT LIKE FEUDAL LORDS AND SERFS, BUT THE BASIC IDEA STILL HELPS US MAKE SENSE OF THE CROSS: IT WAS MAINLY FOR GOD'S BENEFIT, NOT THE DEVIL'S.

HEY, WHAT ABOUT GIVING THE DEVIL HIS DUE?

FINALLY, FOR ALL HIS COMMITMENT TO RATIONALITY AND HIS PASSION FOR THINKING, ANSELM KNEW THAT UNDERSTANDING AND FAITH HAD TO WORK TOGETHER. IN FACT, HE EXPRESSED THIS IDEA IN ITS CLASSIC FORM, SAYING THAT THEOLOGY IS "*FIDES QUAERENS INTELLECTUM,*" OR "FAITH SEEKING UNDERSTANDING." AS HE PUT IT IN ONE OF HIS LONG, WRITTEN, PHILOSOPHICAL PRAYERS TO GOD:

I LONG TO UNDERSTAND IN SOME DEGREE THY TRUTH, WHICH MY HEART BELIEVES AND LOVES. FOR I DO NOT SEEK TO UNDERSTAND THAT I MAY BELIEVE, BUT I BELIEVE IN ORDER TO UNDERSTAND.

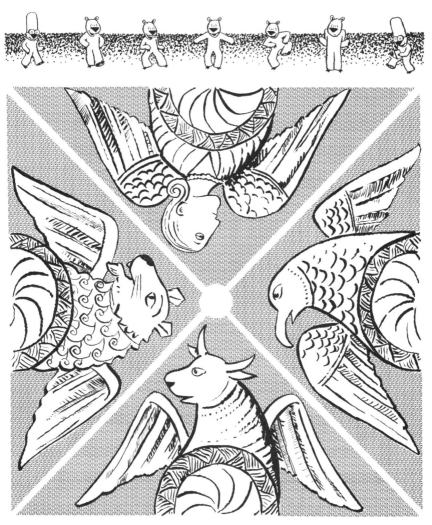

TETRA-MORPH

ASK DR. DOCTRINE

RIGHT DOCTRINE, RIGHT NOW!

DEAR DOC,

TELL ME ABOUT THIS "GLORY" BUSINESS.

GOOD QUESTION!

GLORY IS THE BIBLE'S WAY OF TALKING ABOUT HOW GOD EXISTS; ABOUT GOD'S BASIC MODE OF BEING. GLORY IS GOD BEHAVING, OR ACTING IN HIS OWN DISTINCTIVE AND CHARACTERISTIC WAY. ONLY GOD HAS THIS KIND OF GLORY!

THE OLD TESTAMENT WORD FOR GLORY, "KABOD," REFERS TO SOMETHING HEAVY, THE WEIGHTINESS OR HEAVINESS THAT CAUSES YOU TO TAKE SOMETHING WITH COMPLETE SERIOUSNESS! LIKE A BEAUTY OR GRANDEUR SO BIG THAT IT WEIGHS DOWN ON YOU!

HEAVY, MAN!

WHICH BRINGS ME TO THE BEST ANALOGY FOR GOD'S GLORY: GLORY IS THE DIVINE BEAUTY. GOD IS BEAUTIFUL IN A WAY NOTHING ELSE COULD POSSIBLY BE! THE DIVINE BEAUTY MUST BE THE GREATEST BEAUTY POSSIBLE...EXCEEDING ALL OUR IMAGININGS OR IDEAS!

SO WHERE DO YOU LOOK TO ACTUALLY SEE THIS BEAUTY? THERE ARE NO PAINTINGS OF IT...AND IT'S NOT THE SAME AS THE BEAUTY OF THE NATURAL WORLD....

THE ANSWER PROBABLY WON'T SURPRISE YOU! WE SEE GOD'S BEAUTY, HIS GLORY, REVEALED IN THE ONE WHO IS THE IMAGE OF THE INVISIBLE GOD! GOD'S SELF-REVELATION...

JESUS CHRIST!

SO, AS PAUL SAYS, GOD HAS SHONE IN OUR HEARTS TO GIVE THE LIGHT OF THE KNOWLEDGE OF THE GLORY OF GOD IN THE FACE OF CHRIST!

(II COR. 4:6)

THAT'S MY ANSWER!

WELL, THERE'S NO WAY TO EASE INTO THIS: THE BOOK OF EZEKIEL STARTS OUT BY DESCRIBING A VISION THAT CAME TO THE PROPHET ONE DAY BY THE RIVER CHEBAR: HE SAW A BIG SWIRLY KIND OF...WELL... A SORT OF WINGED, SPINNING...A, UH, A GLOWING THING SORT OF LIKE A HOT COAL, WITH SIX WINGS AND FOUR HEADS, EXCEPT REALLY SIXTEEN HEADS, AND WHEELS WITHIN WHEELS WITH EYEBALLS AND THEY LOOKED LIKE DIFFERENT ANIMALS FLYING IN FORMATION...I THINK.

IT LOOKED KIND OF LIKE THIS, MAYBE...

And as coming from the cloud with fire flashing forth continually, and a bright light around it, and in its midst something like glowing metal in the midst of the fire. And within it there were figures resembling four living beings. And this was their appearance: they had human form. And their legs were straight and their feet were like a calf's hoof, and they gleamed like burnished bronze. Under their wings on their four sides were human hands. As for the faces and wings of the four of them, their wings touched one another; their faces did not turn when they moved, each went straight forward. As for the form of their faces, each had the face of a man, all four had the face ...

WHATEVER IT IS THAT HE SAW, IT MADE *QUITE* AN IMPRESSION ON HIM. IT WASN'T JUST A *VAGUE* FEELING OF HOLINESS, BUT SOME KIND OF SURGING, RADIANT PLENITUDE OF NATURAL *FORMS!*

SPECIFICALLY, HE WAS STRUCK BY THE *FOUR FACES* OF THE *CREATURES:* HUMAN, LION, OX AND EAGLE.

IN REVELATION, *JOHN* SAW SOMETHING VERY SIMILAR, THOUGH HE DESCRIBES SOME VERY DIFFERENT THINGS, TOO.

IN JOHN'S VERSION OF THE VISION, THE FOUR CREATURES ARE STANDING BEFORE THE THRONE OF GOD, CRYING OUT, "HOLY, HOLY, HOLY!" THEY SEEM TO BE SOME KIND OF ANGELIC BEINGS, A SORT OF SUPER-SERAPH BEARING WITNESS TO GOD'S GLORY AND ALWAYS GIVING PRAISE.

DID YOU SEE A BUNCH OF WHEELS?

NO. DID YOU SEE ALL THOSE OLD GUYS WITH CROWNS?

NO. DID YOU SEE THE THINGS WITH ANIMAL HEADS?

YES!

CHRISTIAN *ARTISTS* HAVE PICKED UP ON THE DETAILS OF THE VISION, AND HAVE USED THE *FOUR-FACED THING*, KNOWN AS THE *"TETRAMORPH,"* IN PAINTINGS, CARVINGS, WEAVING, DRAWINGS, AND STAINED GLASS FOR CENTURIES!

NORMALLY, THE *TETRAMORPH* IS USED AS A DECORATIVE *SYMBOL* FOR GOD'S *GLORY* AND *HOLINESS*. OFTEN IT WILL APPEAR JUST UNDERNEATH A DRAWING OF GOD OR CHRIST SEATED ON A *THRONE.*

VERY EARLY ON, THOUGH, THE FOUR CREATURES WERE *SPLIT APART,* AND USUALLY PLACED IN THE FOUR CORNERS OF A PAGE. BUT THINGS *REALLY* START TO GET *INTERESTING* WHEN EACH OF THE FOUR CREATURES CAME TO BE ASSOCIATED WITH EACH OF THE FOUR *GOSPELS!* WHY DID THIS HAPPEN?

MATTHEW

MARK

LUKE

JOHN

THE *HUMAN* FACE, OR A MAN WITH WINGS, CAME TO BE ASSOCIATED WITH *MATTHEW'S* GOSPEL. THIS IS PROBABLY BECAUSE MATTHEW BEGINS WITH A *GENEALOGY*, EMPHASIZING THE *HUMAN* LINEAGE OF JESUS. THE MAJOR EVENT THAT IS UNDERLINED BY THIS COMBINATION IS JESUS' HUMAN BIRTH, OR THE INCARNATION.

THE *EAGLE* WAS LINKED TO *JOHN*, BECAUSE JOHN'S GOSPEL SORT OF TAKES A *BIRDS-EYE VIEW* OF JESUS' MINISTRY, REPORTING HIS STATEMENTS LIKE "I AM THE WAY," ETC. JOHN WROTE THE MOST BLATANTLY THEOLOGICAL GOSPEL, IN OTHER WORDS. THE MAJOR EVENT THE EAGLE SYMBOLIZES IS JESUS' ASCENSION INTO HEAVEN.

...AZOR, ZADOK, ACHIM, ELIUD, ELEAZAR, MATTHAN, JACOB, JOSEPH... IS THAT 13 OR 14?

12. HERE, YOU WANT A BACKRUB?

DO YOU THINK MY CHAPTERS ARE TOO LONG? HONESTLY.

NO! THEY'RE GREAT! YOU PUT A LOT INTO THEM!

I THINK THOSE OTHER GUYS ARE COPYING OFF OF ME!

DON'T WORRY ABOUT IT!

HOW DO YOU SPELL *CRUCIFIXION?*

SEE, ARE, YOU, SEE, EYE, EFF, EYE, EX, EYE, OH, ENN.

MARK GOT THE *LION*, MAYBE BECAUSE HIS GOSPEL IS AS BRIEF AND *TO THE POINT* AS A LION ON THE HUNT! OR MAYBE BECAUSE HE BEGINS WITH JOHN THE BAPTIST, "A VOICE CRYING IN THE WILDERNESS" LIKE A LION'S ROARING. ANYWAY, BACK THEN PEOPLE BELIEVED THAT LION CUBS WERE *BORN DEAD* AND RESUSCITATED ON THE *THIRD DAY*, SO THE LION SYMBOLIZES CHRIST'S *RESURRECTION!*

THE *OX* WAS PAIRED UP WITH *LUKE*, BECAUSE THE OX IS A SACRIFICIAL ANIMAL, AND LUKE IS SAID TO PAY SPECIAL ATTENTION TO THE *DEATH* OF JESUS. OBVIOUSLY THE MAJOR EVENT OF JESUS' LIFE THAT IS HIGHLIGHTED BY THIS COMBINATION IS THE *CRUCIFIXION.*

NOW YOU CAN'T TAKE THE *COMBINATIONS* TOO SERIOUSLY, BECAUSE THEY SEEM A LITTLE *CONTRIVED.* ALSO, THE FIRST PERSON TO EXPLAIN THEM, *IRENAEUS,* HAD GOOD REASONS WHY *MARK* IS THE *EAGLE* AND *JOHN* IS THE *LION!*

MATT.
MAN

MARK
LION

LUKE
OX

JOHN
EAG.

AND THEN *ATHANASIUS* GAVE *LUKE* THE LION. AND *MARK* THE *OX.* BUT *AUGUSTINE* SAID THAT THE *LION* WENT TO *MATTHEW,* BUT THE *MAN* WITH WINGS BELONGS WITH *MARK.* FINALLY IN THE *MIDDLE AGES* THINGS SETTLED DOWN LIKE I EXPLAINED THEM THE *FIRST* TIME.

IT LOOKS TO ME LIKE YOU CAN ASSIGN *ANY* ANIMAL TO *ANY* EVANGELIST. I MEAN, *WHO SAYS* LUKE EMPHASIZES THE *CROSS* MORE THAN MARK OR MATTHEW?

MATT.
MAN

MARK
LION

OX

JOHN
EAG.

SO IF THE COMBINATIONS ARE *ARBITRARY,* WHAT ARE WE SUPPOSED TO *LEARN* FROM THESE FOUR CREATURES?

WELL...

IF YOU'LL LISTEN FOR A MINUTE, WE COULD TELL YOU ALL ABOUT IT!

THE FOUR LIVING CREATURES!

YOU SHOULD SEE 'EM WHEN THEY'VE GOT THE WHEELS!

WHEN WE'RE REPRESENTED, WE'RE USUALLY SURROUNDING THE EXALTED, *ALL-POWERFUL CHRIST* ON THE THRONE OF *JUDGMENT!* BUT BECAUSE WE'RE *ALSO* LINKED WITH THE FOUR GOSPELS...

WE'RE SUPPOSED TO *REMIND* YOU THAT THE ALMIGHTY *SON OF GOD* IS THE SAME JESUS WHO THE *GOSPELS* TELL ABOUT; THE HUMBLE *SERVANT* WHO WALKED AMONG US DOING HIS *FATHER'S* WILL!

GRRR!

IT'S THAT JESUS GUY AGAIN!

HEY, MR. JESUS! ARE YOU *REALLY* A RABBI?

HE'S COOL!

I CALL DIBS ON HIS LAP!

GROUP HUG!

ME NEXT! ME NEXT!

IS HE GIVING OUT CANDY?

SUFFER US! SUFFER US!

IS THAT THAT JESUS GUY I BEEN HEARING ABOUT?

ME FIRST!

BLESS MY BABY NOW!

SO THE TETRAMORPH IS A SYMBOLIC WAY OF SHOWING THAT THE *GLORY OF GOD...*

IS FOUND IN *JESUS CHRIST!*

AND WHEN WE TRY TO THINK ABOUT GOD ALMIGHTY, AND HIS *POWER* AND *GLORY* AND *KINGDOM,* OUR BEST GUIDES WILL ALWAYS BE...

MATTHEW!

MARK! I MEAN "GRRR!"

LUKE!

AND JOHN!

THE END

33

MEET THE THEOLOGIANS
KARL BARTH

(1886-1968)

KARL BARTH IS PROBABLY THE MOST IMPORTANT PROTESTANT THEOLOGIAN OF THE TWENTIETH CENTURY. HE WAS A PASTOR IN SWITZERLAND WHO FOUND THAT THE LIBERAL THEOLOGY HE LEARNED IN SEMINARY WAS COMPLETELY IRRELEVANT TO THE ACTUAL NEEDS OF HIS CONGREGATION. EVEN MORE SHOCKING, HE FOUND THAT IT DID NOT MATCH UP WITH WHAT HE FOUND IN THE SCRIPTURES!

BONG!

ONCE WHEN HE WAS A BOY, HE STUMBLED WHILE CLIMBING A DARK CHURCH TOWER'S STAIRS. WHEN HE REACHED OUT FOR THE HANDRAIL, HE GRABBED THE BELL-ROPE INSTEAD! LATER HE COMPARED THIS EVENT WITH THE IMPACT OF HIS 1919 COMMENTARY ON ROMANS, WHICH CAUSED AN INCREDIBLE UPROAR: IN TRYING TO GET HIS OWN FOOTING, HE ACCIDENTALLY WOKE UP THE WHOLE COUNTRYSIDE!

IF ANYONE TOOK THE TASK OF THEOLOGY AS SERIOUSLY AS IT DESERVES, IT WAS BARTH. HE WAS FULLY AWARE OF JUST HOW IMPOSSIBLE IT IS FOR ANY PERSON TO SPEAK ABOUT GOD WITH SUFFICIENT AUTHORITY AND HOW CAREFUL THEOLOGIANS NEED TO BE EVEN WHEN THEY TAKE REVELATION AS THEIR STARTING POINT. IN 1928 HE WROTE THE FIRST VOLUME OF A SYSTEMATIC THEOLOGY, BUT AFTER IT WAS PUBLISHED, HE REGRETTED MUCH OF WHAT HE HAD SAID. SO HE REFUSED TO ALLOW IT TO BE REPRINTED, AND INSTEAD HE STARTED OVER.

BY 1932 HE WAS MORE SURE OF HIS PROCEDURE, AND HE STARTED PUBLISHING HIS GREATEST WORK, THE CHURCH DOGMATICS. FOR THE NEXT THREE DECADES HE CONTINUED TO WORK ON THIS SET OF BOOKS. ALTHOUGH HE DIED BEFORE HE COULD FINISH THEM, HE MANAGED TO PRODUCE 13 VOLUMES, OR ABOUT TEN THOUSAND PAGES. THEY ARE STILL IN PRINT.

THE MOVEMENT BARTH STARTED IS SOMETIMES CALLED "NEO-ORTHODOXY." HE AND HIS COHORTS BROUGHT BACK DOCTRINES WHICH HAD FALLEN OUT OF FAVOR WITH THE MAINSTREAM OF THEOLOGIANS: THE VIRGIN BIRTH, ESCHATOLOGY, THE RESURRECTION, AND THE DOCTRINE OF THE TRINITY.

I VAS TRINITARIAN VEN TRINITARIANISM VASN'T COOL!

BARTH'S WORK CAN BE SUMMED UP IN THE PHRASE "CHRIST-CENTERED." WITH INCREASING THOROUGHNESS HE INSISTED ON THINKING THROUGH EVERY ASPECT OF CHRISTIAN FAITH IN ITS DIRECT RELATIONSHIP TO JESUS CHRIST, AND ROOTING OUT EVERYTHING ABSTRACT THAT MIGHT TRY TO TAKE THE PLACE OF CENTRALITY AWAY FROM JESUS CHRIST.

THE MEANING OF GOD'S DEITY --THE ONLY *TRUE* DEITY IN THE NEW TESTAMENT SENSE-- *CANNOT* BE GATHERED FROM ANY NOTION OF SUPREME, ABSOLUTE, NON-WORLD-LY BEING. IT CAN BE LEARNED *ONLY* FROM WHAT TOOK PLACE IN *CHRIST*.

THE MOSAIC CREATION

SEE? "THE EARTH WAS A *FORMLESS* VOID AND *DARKNESS* COVERED THE FACE OF THE DEEP, WHILE THE *SPIRIT* OF *GOD* SWEPT OVER THE FACE OF THE WATERS." AND HERE'S THE SPIRIT OF GOD!

HEY, THE BIBLE DOESN'T SAY, "IN THE BEGINNING WAS A *BIRD*." WHAT'S UP WITH THE DOVE?

GOOD QUESTION!

WHERE *ELSE* IS THERE A STORY ABOUT A *DOVE* WHO BRINGS THE PROMISE OF *NEW LIFE* TO A WORLD DROWNING IN A *FLOOD* OF CHAOS?

OBJECTION! THE PROSECUTION IS *LEADING* THE WITNESS!

OVER-RULED!

NOAH'S ARK! THE DOVE FLIES OVER THE FLOOD IN THAT STORY!

RIGHT! AND THEN IN THE NEW TESTAMENT, AS *JESUS* IS *BAPTIZED* IN THE JORDAN, THE HOLY SPIRIT *DESCENDS* IN THE FORM OF A DOVE ON HIM!

OH, SO THE ARTIST PUT THE DOVE HERE TO *LINK UP* ALL THOSE IDEAS, YOU THINK?

PROBABLY!

MY, THAT'S A *SOPHISTICATED* INTERTEXTUAL READING!

I ALWAYS THOUGHT THE HOLY SPIRIT WAS SORT OF A *CAGED* LITTLE SONGBIRD CONFINED TO CHURCHES. BUT *THIS* BIRD GOES WHEREVER HE WANTS TO! HE'S *IN CHARGE!*

THAT'S NO *TAME* BIRD!

AND GOD SAID, "LET THERE BE *LIGHT,*" AND THERE WAS LIGHT. THEN GOD JUDGES THE LIGHT TO BE *GOOD,* AND SEPARATES IT FROM THE *DARKNESS.*

THAT'S SUPPOSED TO BE *GOD?* IT LOOKS MORE LIKE *JESUS* TO ME!

NOW *HANG ON* A MINUTE, HERE!

RIGHT. YOU CAN TELL BY THE *CROSS* IN HIS *HALO!*

WELL, *GENESIS* DOESN'T SAY ANYTHING ABOUT IT BEING *JESUS* WHO DID THE CREATING!

NO, BUT IT SAYS, "GOD *SAID...*" AND THAT MEANS GOD SPOKE A *WORD.* AND *WHO* IS THE *WORD* OF GOD?

JESUS!

OHHHH, *THAT'S* WHY JOHN'S *GOSPEL* STARTS OUT, "IN THE BEGINNING WAS THE *WORD...*"

EXACTLY! AND ALSO. IT SOLVES THE PROBLEM OF HOW TO *DRAW* GOD THE CREATOR: WE CAN DRAW *JESUS,* AND IT GIVES US SOMETHING TO *PICTURE.*

WHY NOT JUST DRAW GOD THE *FATHER?*

WELL, YOU *COULD,* I GUESS. *MICHELANGELO* DID, IN THE SISTINE CHAPEL IN ROME!

WHAT DO YOU THINK OF IT?

AAAARGH! PUT IT *AWAY!* PUT IT *AWAY!*

I KIND OF LIKE IT...

GOD BOWLS?

BY THE WAY, DID ANYBODY NOTICE THAT WE'VE GOT THE *TRINITY* HERE IN THIS STORY? *GOD* (THE *FATHER*), WHOSE *SPIRIT* IS MOVING ON THE WATER, SPEAKS HIS WORD (THE *SON*), AND THE WORLD IS *CREATED*.

WOW!

EVEN ALLOWING FOR THE OBVIOUS PROJECTION OF LATER DOCTRINAL CONSTRUCTS BACK ONTO THE EXEGESIS OF THIS TEXT, I AGREE THAT YOUR READING IS A COMPELLING OPTION!

HEY, WHAT'S WITH THIS BIG *CIRCLE?*

IT'S "THE *FIRMAMENT:*" THE BIG *ASTRO-DOME* THAT KEEPS THE ATMOSPHERE TOGETHER.

BUT THERE'S NO *DOME* IN THE SKY!

WORKS FOR *ME!*

WELL, WHAT SHAPE DO *YOU* THINK THE SKY IS?

GOD'S *ALWAYS* PROVIDING *SHELTER* FOR US!

HEY, NOW THERE'S *TWO* ANGELS!

LOOKS LIKE WE'RE GOING TO BE GETTING *ONE* ANGEL PER *DAY* FROM HERE ON IN!

THAT'LL HELP US KEEP *COUNT*, AT LEAST!

HOW *HANDY!*

DAY THREE: **PLANTS!**

THREE ANGELS!

SUPER COOL!

"GOD SAID, 'LET THE **EARTH** BRING FORTH VEGETATION.'" AND DID IT **EVER!**

HEY, THAT'S **NEAT!** GOD DIDN'T JUST SAY, 'LET THERE BE PLANTS!' HE LET THE EARTH, WHICH HE HAD **ALREADY** MADE, GET INVOLVED IN THE WORK TOO!

HEY, I NEVER NOTICED **THAT** BEFORE!

BUT I THOUGHT GOD MADE EVERYTHING FROM **NOTHING!**

SURE: BEFORE GOD **STARTED** MAKING, THERE WAS **NOTHING** AT ALL. BUT **MOST** OF THE CREATION STORY IS ABOUT WHAT GOD **DID** WITH WHAT HE **ALREADY** MADE:

HE **SEPARATES** THINGS, **NAMES** THEM, **EVALUATES** THEM AND GIVES SOME OF THEM A **ROLE** TO PLAY IN THE **ONGOING DEVELOPMENT** OF THE CREATED WORLD! HE GETS REALLY **INVOLVED** WITH THE THINGS HE MAKES AND **WORKS** ON THEM LIKE A SKILLED **CRAFTSMAN!** HE'S NOT EVEN **NERVOUS** ABOUT **SHARING** SOME OF HIS JOBS WITH HIS CREATURES!

LATER ON, HE'LL EVEN LET **HUMANS** GET INVOLVED IN THE GARDENING AND NAMING.

GOD LOVES HIS CREATION **SO** MUCH!

41

"AND GOD SAID, LET THERE BE *LIGHTS* IN THE DOME OF THE SKY... LET THEM BE FOR SIGNS AND FOR SEASON AND DAYS AND YEARS... AND GOD MADE THE TWO *GREAT LIGHTS*," THE BIG ONE TO RULE THE DAY, AND THE LESSER ONE TO RULE THE NIGHT!

SO THE STARS AND THE PLANETS *RULE* OVER US?

WELL, WE CERTAINLY *DEPEND* ON THE SUN AND MOON TO KEEP US *ALIVE*, DON'T WE?

YEAH, BUT IT SOUNDS LIKE GOD MADE THEM OUR *BOSSES* AND THE STARS *RUN* OUR *LIVES!*

OH NO, NOT LIKE *THAT!* THIS RULES OUT *ASTROLOGY ALTOGETHER:* THE STARS ARE NOT GODS; THEY ARE *CREATURES* OF THE ONLY TRUE GOD! OUR LIVES ARE DETERMINED BY *GOD*, NOT BY SOME STELLAR *LAWS* OR *FATE!*

COOL! WHAT'S YOUR *SIGN?*

"TAURUS," YOU IDIOT.

AM I GIVEN TO UNDERSTAND THAT THERE WERE *PLANTS* BEFORE THERE WAS A *SUN?* THIS SEEMS *IMPOSSIBLE,* SINCE THERE WOULD BE NO BASIS FOR *PHOTOSYNTHESIS...*

ARE YOU LOOKIN' FER *TROUBLE,* BUDDY?

YET ON THE OTHER HAND, THE NOTION OF *"LIGHT"* BEFORE THE *"LIGHTS"* SEEMS CONSONANT WITH THE DISCOVERY OF THE *BACKGROUND* LUMINOSITY PRESENT IN THE UNIVERSE, NOT *LOCALIZED* IN STELLAR BODIES....

YOU JUST MAKE YER LITTLE *THEORIES* WORK OUT ANY WAY YOU *HAVE TO,* PAL, BUT DON'T *MESS* WITH MY BIBLE!

43

NOW ON THE **SAME** DAY AS ALL THE LAND ANIMALS GOD **ALSO** MADE THE **HUMAN RACE!**

JUST ANOTHER **ANIMAL?**

WELL, THERE ARE SOME **DIFFERENCES** HERE: INSTEAD OF TELLING THE **EARTH** TO BRING FORTH HUMANS, GOD TAKES A MOMENT TO **DELIBERATE** ABOUT THIS NEXT BIG MOVE: "LET US MAKE HUMANITY IN **OUR IMAGE.**" AND THEN HE **DOES.**

IF YOU JUMP **AHEAD** TO THE **NEXT** CHAPTER, YOU GET THE **REST** OF THE STORY: GOD **FORMED** THE FIRST MAN FROM THE DUST OF THE EARTH. SO HERE THE ARTIST SHOWS US GOD **KNEADING** THE CLAY, GIVING **SHAPE** TO THE HUMAN BEING.

AND THEN THE LORD "**BREATHED** INTO HIS NOSTRILS THE **BREATH OF LIFE;** AND THE MAN BECAME A **LIVING BEING.**"

GOLLY!

THERE'S THE **SPIRIT** AGAIN: THE **BREATH** OF GOD, GIVING **LIFE!**

HEY, DOES THIS MEAN **EVERYBODY'S** GOT THE **HOLY SPIRIT** LIVING INSIDE OF THEM?

WELL, IT MEANS THAT **ONLY** GOD'S CREATIVE POWER KEEPS **ANYBODY** ALIVE AND BREATHING. BUT THAT'S **DIFFERENT** FROM THE NEW TESTAMENT EXPERIENCE OF **RECEIVING** THE HOLY SPIRIT FROM **JESUS.** THAT'S SOMETHING YOU HAVE TO **ASK** FOR, AND **WANT!**

44

45

MEET THE THEOLOGIANS

BASIL "THE GREAT" 329-379

BASIL OF CAESAREA, USUALLY CALLED BASIL THE GREAT, WAS ONE OF ELEVEN CHILDREN BORN IN A WEALTHY CHRISTIAN FAMILY IN CAPPADOCIA (ASIA MINOR). AND WHAT A FAMILY: THREE OF HIS SIBLINGS ARE CONSIDERED SAINTS, AND HIS MOTHER'S PARENTS ENDURED FIERCE ANTI-CHRISTIAN PERSECUTION, FLEEING FOR THEIR LIVES. HIS MOM AND SISTER (BOTH NAMED MACRINA) TUTORED HIM IN THE FAITH AND PREPARED HIM FOR THE BEST SCHOOLS.

BASIL WAS THE OLDEST AND MOST PROMINENT OF THE THREE BISHOPS KNOWN AS THE CAPPADOCIAN FATHERS. THE OTHER TWO WERE BOTH NAMED GREGORY: GREGORY OF NYSSA WAS BASIL'S YOUNGER BROTHER, AND GREGORY OF NAZIANZUS WAS HIS BEST FRIEND FROM COLLEGE. AT BASIL'S INITIATIVE THESE THREE MEN FOUNDED A NEW CHRISTIANIZED CULTURE IN THE GREEK WORLD AND MADE PERMANENT CONTRIBUTIONS TO THE CHURCH'S THEOLOGY, LITURGY AND MONASTIC LIFE. THEIR INFLUENCE WAS VAST!

ONE OF BASIL'S MOST IMPORTANT CONTRIBUTIONS TO THE CHURCH'S DOCTRINE WAS IN HIS TEACHING ON THE TRINITY. MORE THAN ANYONE BEFORE HIM BASIL HAD A VERY CLEAR UNDERSTANDING THAT IT IS EQUALLY IMPORTANT TO DISCERN THE THREE PERSONS IN GOD AS IT IS TO RECALL THAT GOD IS ONLY ONE IN ESSENCE. HE ESTABLISHED THE FORMULA "GOD IS THREE PERSONS IN ONE NATURE."

BASIL PREACHED A SERIES OF SERMONS ON THE SIX DAYS OF CREATION, THE HEXAEMERON. IN THESE IMPORTANT MESSAGE HE ESTABLISHED THE DIFFERENCE BETWEEN THE OLD PAGAN IDEA ABOUT THE WORLD, AND THE NEW, AUTHENTICALLY CHRISTIAN UNDERSTANDING OF IT. CHRISTIANS BELIEVE THAT GOD CREATED THE WORLD AS A GOOD, ORDERLY FINITE REALITY. THE WORLD IS NOT A NATURAL EXTENSION OF GOD'S OWN BEING, NOR IS IT MADE OF EVIL MATERIAL.

BASIL'S HEXAEMERON IS REMARKABLE FOR MANY REASONS: IT IS A CAREFUL STUDY OF THE BIBLICAL TEXT ITSELF, SHOWING ALSO A GENUINE LOVE AND ADMIRATION FOR THE RICHNESS OF THE CREATION. FURTHERMORE, BASIL MADE USE OF THE BEST IDEAS THE SCIENCE OF HIS DAY HAD TO OFFER HIM. FOR INSTANCE, HE ENGAGES IN A DEBATE ABOUT WHAT KEEPS THE ROUND BALL OF THE WORLD HANGING IN ITS PLACE.

HE WAS A DEVOUT THINKER WHO RELISHED THE EXPERIENCE OF PRAYER AND CONTEMPLATION. HE ALSO MADE A GREAT CONTRIBUTION TO THE DOCTRINE OF THE HOLY SPIRIT: HIS TEACHINGS ABOUT THE SPIRIT BECAME THE OFFICIAL TEXT OF THE NICENE CREED: "WE BELIEVE IN THE HOLY SPIRIT, THE LORD AND GIVER OF LIFE, WHO PROCEEDS FROM THE FATHER, WHO IS WORSHIPED AND GLORIFIED TOGETHER WITH THE FATHER AND THE SON."

THE SPIRIT IS THE *PLACE* OF THEM THAT ARE BEING *SANCTIFIED*... THE SPIRIT IS TRULY THE PLACE OF THE *SAINTS*, AND THE *SAINT* IS THE PROPER PLACE FOR THE *SPIRIT*, BEING GOD'S *TEMPLE*.

THEO & DEMPFEY'S WORD PAGE

IT'S A TINY *LEXICON* TO HELP YOU WITH *APPOSITE* EXPRESSIONS.

REALLY WHAT IT *IS*, IS A *WORD PAGE*!

REVELATION

FROM THE GREEK WORD, *"APOKOLYPS,"* MEANING *"UNVEILING."* REVELATION REFERS TO DIVINE *DISCLOSURE,* AND TAKES MANY *FORMS,* INCLUDING, OF COURSE, THE *VERBAL.*

IT'S WHEN GOD *SHOWS* YOU SOMETHING. HE ALREADY *DID* A BUNCH OF THIS IN THE *BIBLE,* SO READ IT *GOOD.*

IMAGINATION

IMAGINATION IS THE MENTAL POWER OF FORMING *CONCEPTS* AND *IMAGES* IN ORDER TO REPRESENT REALITY IN A WAY THAT IS COMPREHENSIBLE AND *MEANINGFUL.* EXERCISE YOURS *FAITHFULLY,* OR IT MAY BEGIN TO *ATROPHY.*

IMAGINATION'S A REAL *GOOD* THING, AS LONG AS YOU DON'T THINK IT MEANS "JUST *MAKING* STUFF *UP.*"

MOSAIC

SAVOR THE DELICIOUS *DOUBLE MEANING* IN THIS WORD: IT IS AN *ART* FORM WHICH INVOLVES USING SMALL COLORED TILES TO FORM A LARGER IMAGE, BUT IT IS ALSO A WORD MEANING "WRITTEN BY *MOSES.*"

OH, I GET IT. IT'S A *JOKE.* IT AIN'T VERY *FUNNY* WHEN YOU HAVE TO EXPLAIN IT.

The Meadow

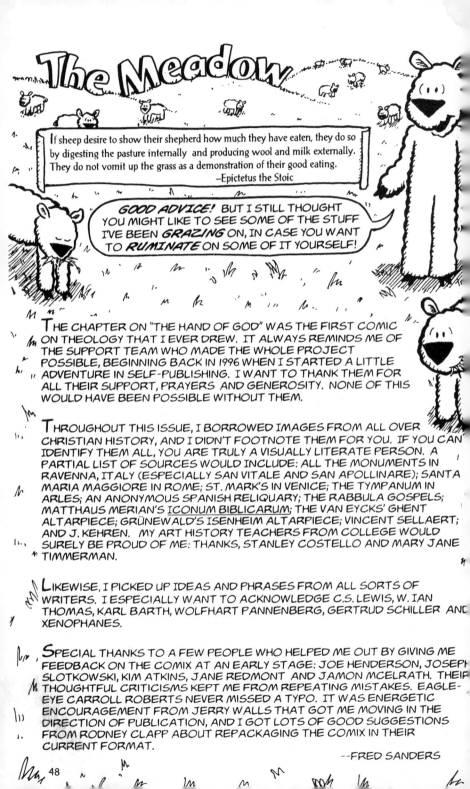

> If sheep desire to show their shepherd how much they have eaten, they do so by digesting the pasture internally and producing wool and milk externally. They do not vomit up the grass as a demonstration of their good eating.
> —Epictetus the Stoic

GOOD ADVICE! BUT I STILL THOUGHT YOU MIGHT LIKE TO SEE SOME OF THE STUFF I'VE BEEN *GRAZING* ON, IN CASE YOU WANT TO *RUMINATE* ON SOME OF IT YOURSELF!

THE CHAPTER ON "THE HAND OF GOD" WAS THE FIRST COMIC ON THEOLOGY THAT I EVER DREW. IT ALWAYS REMINDS ME OF THE SUPPORT TEAM WHO MADE THE WHOLE PROJECT POSSIBLE, BEGINNING BACK IN 1996 WHEN I STARTED A LITTLE ADVENTURE IN SELF-PUBLISHING. I WANT TO THANK THEM FOR ALL THEIR SUPPORT, PRAYERS AND GENEROSITY. NONE OF THIS WOULD HAVE BEEN POSSIBLE WITHOUT THEM.

THROUGHOUT THIS ISSUE, I BORROWED IMAGES FROM ALL OVER CHRISTIAN HISTORY, AND I DIDN'T FOOTNOTE THEM FOR YOU. IF YOU CAN IDENTIFY THEM ALL, YOU ARE TRULY A VISUALLY LITERATE PERSON. A PARTIAL LIST OF SOURCES WOULD INCLUDE: ALL THE MONUMENTS IN RAVENNA, ITALY (ESPECIALLY SAN VITALE AND SAN APOLLINARE); SANTA MARIA MAGGIORE IN ROME; ST. MARK'S IN VENICE; THE TYMPANUM IN ARLES; AN ANONYMOUS SPANISH RELIQUARY; THE RABBULA GOSPELS; MATTHAUS MERIAN'S <u>ICONUM BIBLICARUM</u>; THE VAN EYCKS' GHENT ALTARPIECE; GRÜNEWALD'S ISENHEIM ALTARPIECE; VINCENT SELLAERT; AND J. KEHREN. MY ART HISTORY TEACHERS FROM COLLEGE WOULD SURELY BE PROUD OF ME: THANKS, STANLEY COSTELLO AND MARY JANE TIMMERMAN.

LIKEWISE, I PICKED UP IDEAS AND PHRASES FROM ALL SORTS OF WRITERS. I ESPECIALLY WANT TO ACKNOWLEDGE C.S. LEWIS, W. IAN THOMAS, KARL BARTH, WOLFHART PANNENBERG, GERTRUD SCHILLER AND XENOPHANES.

SPECIAL THANKS TO A FEW PEOPLE WHO HELPED ME OUT BY GIVING ME FEEDBACK ON THE COMIX AT AN EARLY STAGE: JOE HENDERSON, JOSEPH SLOTKOWSKI, KIM ATKINS, JANE REDMONT AND JAMON MCELRATH. THEIR THOUGHTFUL CRITICISMS KEPT ME FROM REPEATING MISTAKES. EAGLE-EYE CARROLL ROBERTS NEVER MISSED A TYPO. IT WAS ENERGETIC ENCOURAGEMENT FROM JERRY WALLS THAT GOT ME MOVING IN THE DIRECTION OF PUBLICATION, AND I GOT LOTS OF GOOD SUGGESTIONS FROM RODNEY CLAPP ABOUT REPACKAGING THE COMIX IN THEIR CURRENT FORMAT.

--FRED SANDERS